Dear Lissie,

May all your dreams be colourful.

lots of love,

Laura
x

Dear Lissie,

May all your dreams be colourful.

Sleep Little Tortoise

L B Baxter

AUSTIN MACAULEY PUBLISHERS™

LONDON • CAMBRIDGE • NEW YORK • SHARJAH

Copyright © L B Baxter (2020)

A CIP catalogue record for this title is available from the British Library.

ISBN 9781528934596 (Paperback)
ISBN 9781528967938 (ePub e-book)

www.austinmacauley.com

First Published (2020)
Austin Macauley Publishers Ltd

25 Canada Square
Canary Wharf
London
E14 5LQ

To Isla

Summer is my favourite time,
It's almost all I see,
For when the trees have shed their leaves,
It's time to sleep for me.

I love to play with all my friends
With the warm sun on my shell,
Listening to the birds as they sing
And wondering what secrets they tell.

There are so many things to discover
And there's so much fun to be had,
The idea of stopping and going to bed
Makes me feel quite sad.

But as the days grow shorter
And winter takes its first peep,
My mum and dad say now it's time
For us to go to sleep.

'I still want to play,' I say to them,
'I'm not going to bed.
Hibernating's boring –
I think I'll stay up instead.'

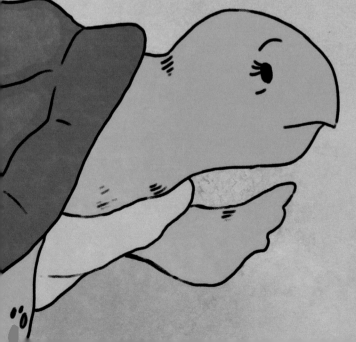

Mum gives me that same old look
And I know what she's going to say,
So I put my claws over my ears
And shout: 'No way! No way! No way!'

'If you don't sleep,' she says to me,
'You'll feel like a fish on dry land,
Like a bird without wings who no longer sings,
I hope you understand.'

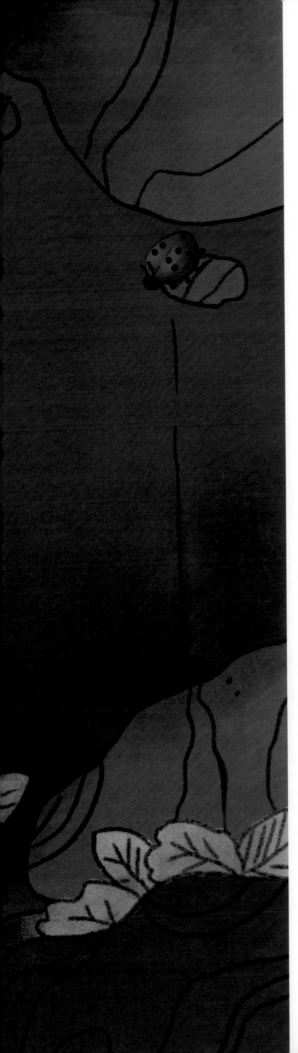

I'd heard this kind of thing before
And I finally agreed to try.
So I settled down and closed my eyes
With a really ginormous sigh.

I lay as quietly as a ladybird crawls
And waited for sleep's warm hug.
But I did not feel it anywhere near,
Not even the slightest tug.

Instead of sleep, questions came
And danced around my head.
I told them this was not the time
And this is what they said:

'Nonsense, this is just the time,
What else have you to do?'
And when I thought about it,
I guess it was quite true.

'So tell me,' they said impatiently,
'Why don't we have wings?
Why do we sleep? Why does it rain?
I need to know these things.'

The questions they went on and on.
Surely Mum would know.
But all she said was: 'No more talking,
Sleep or you won't grow!'

Before long I grew thirsty,
Then desperately needed the loo.
Dad said: 'Now it's time to settle –
Look, here's what you must do.

Paint a picture in your mind,
Add all the things you love;
The greenest grass under your feet,
The bluest sky above.

Find the brightest yellow
And paint a golden sun,
Then step inside with all your friends
And start to have some fun.

Imagine you're a dinosaur
Or that you can fly.
Perhaps your feet are made of springs
And you can touch the sky.

Maybe you could be the wind
That blows the ships at sea.
Or a jolly little mouse
Drinking cups of tea.'

My mind became all floaty
And wandered here and there.
A dreamy world was reaching out
With lots of things to share.

I drifted right up to the moon
With a couple of friendly cats.
We found a party when we arrived,
With the guests in the craziest hats.

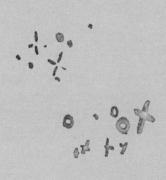

Then suddenly I was on a farm
Surrounded by cows that could talk,
And as if that wasn't strange enough,
They all ate with a knife and fork.

The chickens, I noticed, all seemed to meow
And the horses all sounded like sheep.
A world of silly wonders
Was waiting for me to sleep.

When Spring arrived, the sun came out
And I finally stopped snoring.
Between you and me, I have to admit
Sleep's actually not so boring!